# Tales of
## Wisdom from
# PANCHATANTRA

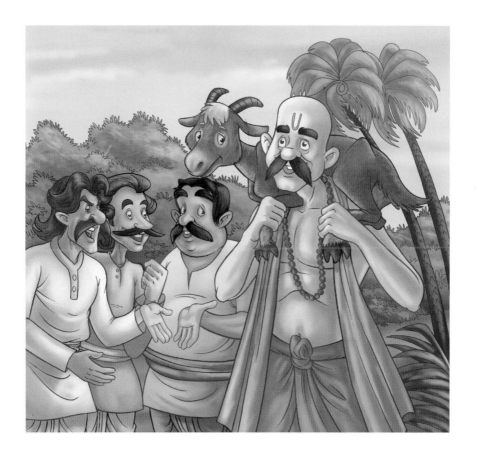

**An imprint of** Om **Books International**

Reprinted in 2017

**An imprint of Om Books International**

Corporate & Editorial Office
A 12, Sector 64, Noida 201 301
Uttar Pradesh, India
Phone: +91 120 477 4100
Email: editorial@ombooks.com
Website: www.ombooksinternational.com

Sales Office
107, Ansari Road, Darya Ganj,
New Delhi 110 002, India
Phone: +91 11 4000 9000
Fax: +91 11 2327 8091
Email: sales@ombooks.com
Website: www.ombooks.com

ISBN: 978-81-87107-89-7

Printed in India

10 9 8 7

# Contents

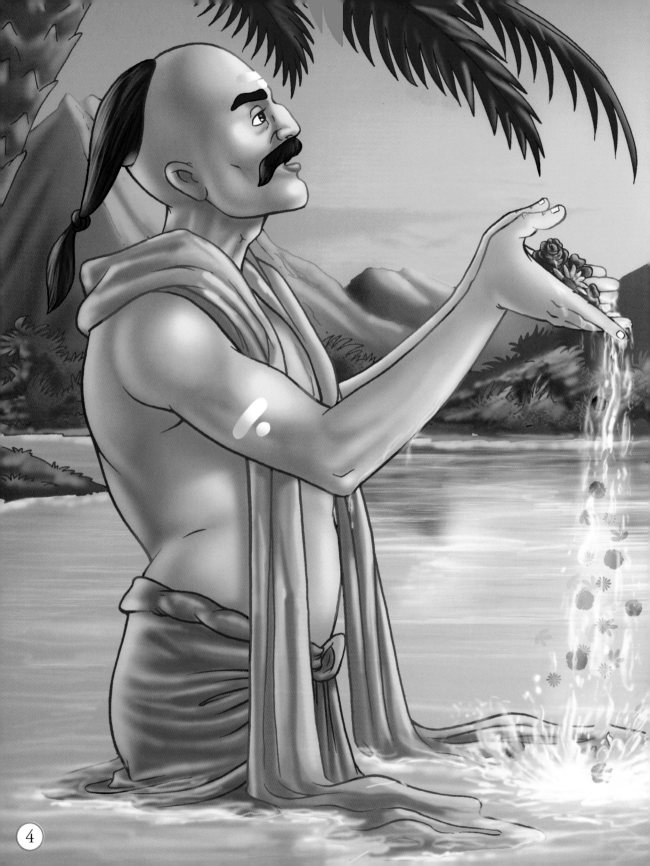

# The Three Crooks

Rishi was a very religious man who lived in a small village. Every morning, he would offer prayers to the Sun God.

Once a rich man from another village invited him to perform a puja ceremony at his house. After feeding him with a good meal, the rich man gifted him a plump goat.

Rishi did not want the goat to walk all the way to his village. So he left the rich man's house after thanking him and carried the goat on his shoulders.

He had to cross the forest to reach his village. On the way three crooks spotted him. They were hungry and had not eaten anything for many days. So, they decided to trick Rishi into dropping the goat.

The first crook went up to Rishi and said, "You look like a religious man. Why would you carry a dog on your shoulders?" Rishi was shocked. He replied, "Are you blind? It is not a dog. It is a goat."

The crook said, "Please continue on your journey if you believe it is a goat. But anyone can see that it is a dog."

Rishi decided to ignore his words and kept walking ahead.

A few minutes later, the second crook approached Rishi. He said, "Is it right for a man like you to carry a dead calf on your shoulders?"

Rishi was surprised as to why the goat did not look like a goat to others. So, he said, "It is not a dead calf. It is a goat young man." The crook replied, "Do you think I would waste my precious time to come and

tell you that it is a dead calf, if that was not really the case?"

Rishi now knew there was something wrong with what he was carrying. After all, two men could not be wrong.

He had taken a few more steps when the third crook came up to him and said, "Why on earth would a man carry a donkey on his shoulders?"

Now that was just the last straw! He dropped the goat on the ground and ran away screaming, "It is a ghost! It is a ghost!

It changes from a goat to a dog to a calf and a donkey!"

The three crooks laughed as they saw Rishi running away, leaving behind the food they had desired.

# The Turtle and the Geese

There was a lovely pool in the middle of a forest. In the pool lived two white geese and a turtle. The geese and the turtle were very good friends.

Sadly, one year, the rains failed. There was no water to be found anywhere. All the plants and trees had dried because of the heat. The pool had also completely dried.

The geese decided to leave the pool and fly away to a greener place. They told the turtle, "Dear friend, we have to give you a sad news. We have decided to fly away to another land, where water is in plenty."

The turtle replied, "My friends, we have been together for so long. How can you leave me and fly away? I will die here without the two of you."

The geese thought for long. They loved their friend, but they had no choice.

One of the geese said to the other, "Surely there must be a way out of this. What if we try to carry the turtle along with us?"

The other goose replied, "How can we? The turtle is too big to sit on our back."

The wise turtle had an answer. He said, "I have an idea! Let me get a stick. You two can hold the ends of the stick in your beaks. I will hold the centre of the stick in my mouth, and hang in the air."

One of the geese said, "That is a good idea, but it is dangerous too. If you open your mouth for any reason, you will fall down and die."

The turtle replied, "Why would I do that if I loved my life?"

So the geese held the stick in their beaks, with the turtle hanging in the centre, and flew away.

After travelling a short distance, the geese flew over a little village where some children were playing in the field.

The children looked up at the sky and laughed and screamed, "Look! Have you ever seen something like this before? Look at the geese and the turtle!"

The turtle was disturbed by all the screaming. He could not understand what was so funny about a turtle being carried to another place by two geese.

The children continued to laugh and shout! The turtle lost his patience and opened his mouth to say, "Why are all of you laughing at me?"

But, it was too late. He fell to the ground because of its foolishness, but did not die.

You know why? Because it was blessed with a hard shell.

The shell developed cracks, and it is believed that since then tortoises have had harder shells.

# A Foolish Offer

Once upon a time, in a jungle lived three friends – jackal, leopard and crow. The three friends served the lion – the king of the jungle.

One day, they found a camel wandering in the forest. One look at the scared camel, the lion took pity on him and said, "Do not be worried,

my friend. From today, you have me as your saviour. You can live here happily, and feed on the grass, which is there in plenty."

The camel was very happy and lived with the three friends.

Unfortunately, the lion got into a fight with a wild elephant. The elephant injured the lion badly, and he became very weak. He could not hunt for himself or the other animals who served him.

The leopard and jackal would hunt food for their master every day, but one day, they were left with nothing to hunt.

They went to the lion and said, "Master, we have searched everywhere, but could not

hunt an animal. Why don't we kill the camel and eat it?"

The lion was very angry. He roared, "Don't you remember that I promised him safety?"

The jackal replied, "My lord! You do not have to kill him. What if he offers himself

to you? If you still do not accept, then remember, you will not be able to live, and all of us will die along with you."

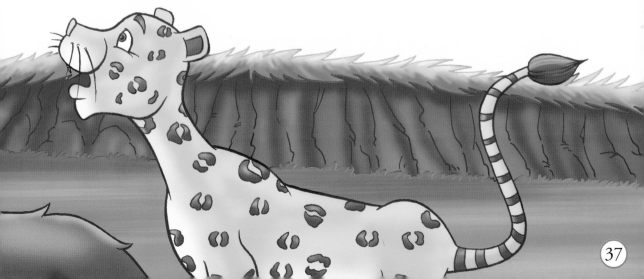

"That is even worse!" said the lion. "If the camel offers himself to me, I will kill him for food, but only if he offers..."

The jackal smiled as he had already made a plan. He called his friends together – the crow, leopard and camel. He said, "Friends,

there is no food for our master for the past few days. He may die of hunger if this continues. I think we should offer ourselves as food one by one." All the animals agreed and went to the lion.

The leopard was the first to begin. He said, "Oh lord! Please kill me and have me as food. That way, all of you will survive." The lion was shocked and said, "You are a part of my family. How can I think of such an act?"

Then it was the jackal's turn. He also made the same offer as the leopard, and the lion denied. The crow was too little to be any animal's food. So, it was finally the turn of the camel.

"The lion has not killed any of his loyal servants. So why would he kill me?" thought the camel, and offered himself to the lion. But to his surprise, the moment he finished making the offer, all the animals jumped on him and killed him.

This just shows one should always be wise and never trust someone blindly.

# The Barber's Folly

Hamid was a merchant. He was rich once upon a time, but had become very poor over the years.

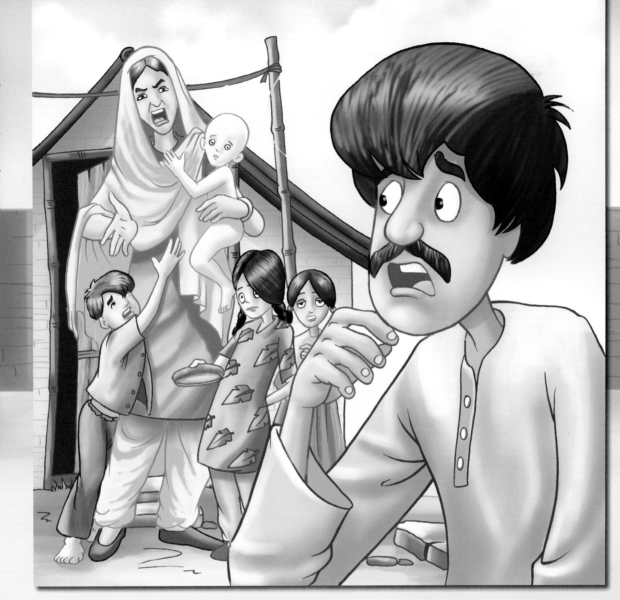

He had a family of four children and could not feed them even once a day. Every morning, his wife would tell him, "Hamid, do something! We need money. We have four children and soon they will die of hunger. Is there nothing you can do to get us food?"

Hamid would go out to find work every single day, but would never be lucky.

One night, he was tired of trying to find work, and was saddened to see his children go to bed hungry. So, he decided that he would kill himself the next day and that would be the only way to be at peace.

Hamid fell asleep with these thoughts and had a strange dream. A monk appeared in his dream. He said, "Hamid, ending your life is no solution. I appear in front of you because of the good deeds of all your ancestors. Tomorrow, I will visit your house. When you see me, strike my head with a stick and I will turn into gold."

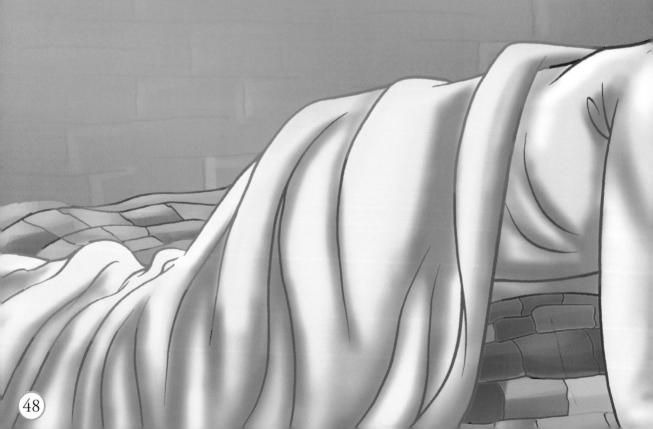

49

Hamid woke up the next day, thinking it was just a dream. That day, Hamid had called the barber to his house. Just as the barber was cutting his hair, there was a knock on the door. When Hamid opened the door, he could not believe his eyes! Standing in front of him was the same monk who had appeared in his dream.

Hamid knew what he had to do. So he fetched a stick from the house and lightly struck the monk on his head. The monk turned into gold.

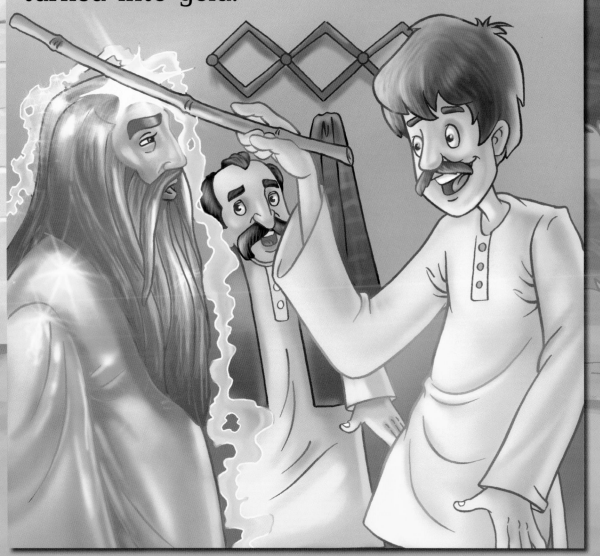

The barber who was watching all this quietly was shocked. He thought to himself, "I never knew that monks can turn into gold when they are hit on the head with a stick!"

Hamid thanked the barber, gave him a bag of gold and said, "My friend, do not tell anyone about what you saw. This is for you and your family. You can now live happily."

But the greedy barber could not sleep that night. He thought, "If all monks can be turned into gold, then I need to invite a few to my house."

So the next morning, the barber went to the monastery near his house.

He met the chief monk and said, "Sir, please visit my house tomorrow with your followers and bless my family." The monk was very pleased with the barber's invitation and agreed to visit him the following day.

The next day, the monks reached the barber's house, who locked them inside his house and before they knew, started striking them with a stick on their heads.

The monks were shocked with what was happening. They pleaded with the barber to stop, but he would not.

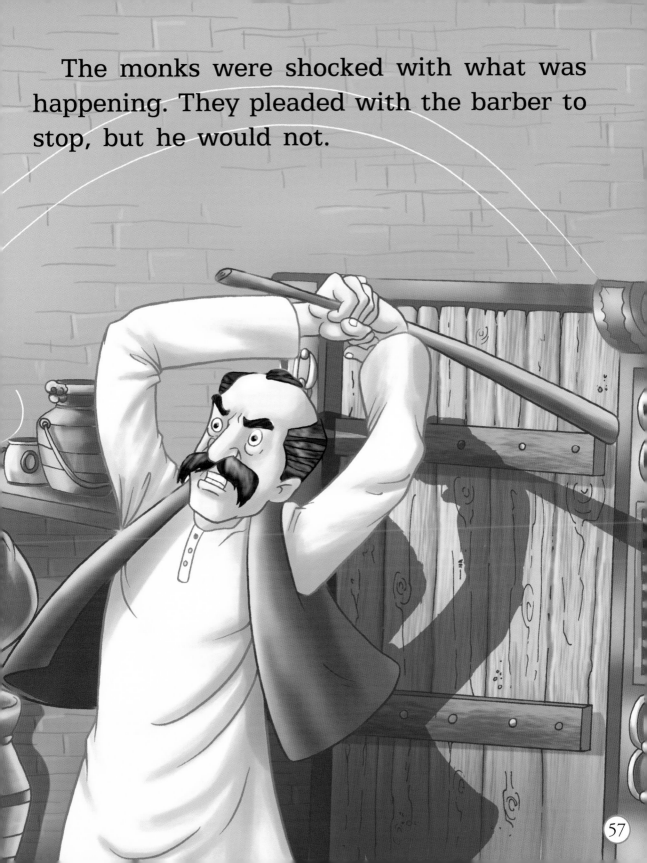

Finally, the monks managed to escape, but were bruised black and blue all over!

The Sheriff who was passing by saw the monks running out. He arrested the barber

for what he had done. The barber was punished to a lifetime in jail. Greed had led the barber to a life of misery.

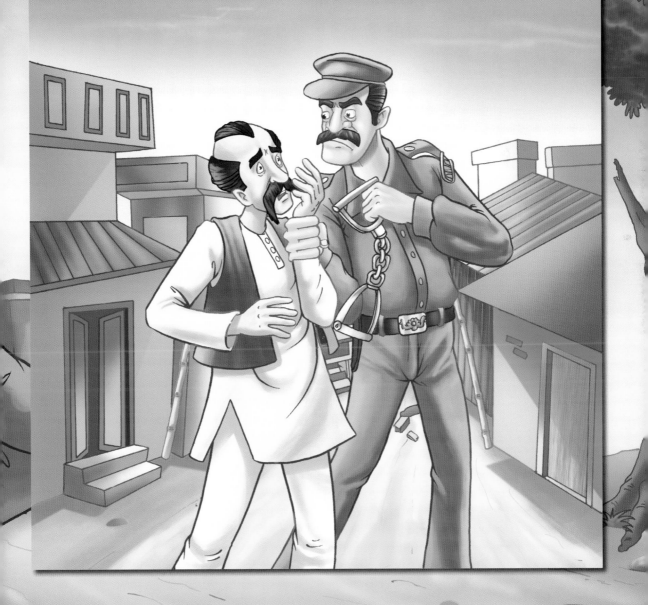

# The Unfaithful Crocodile

There lived a monkey on a big cherry tree near the lake.

One day, a crocodile came out of the lake and rested himself under the tree.

Seeing the crocodile, the monkey was scared and asked, "Who are you? What are you doing under my tree?"

The crocodile replied, "I am a crocodile and I live in the water. I came to see if there was anything to eat here."

The monkey took pity on the crocodile and said, "You are welcome. I would love to be your friend from today. Please eat this sweet fruit." The monkey threw a few cherries at the crocodile. The crocodile enjoyed eating them, and went away happily.

The next day, the crocodile came back to eat. The monkey fed his new friend a lot of cherries. This time, the crocodile carried a few cherries to his wife.

His wife was very happy to eat the cherries. She said, "If the fruit you get from the monkey is so sweet, imagine how sweet would be the heart of the monkey who eats these fruits!"

The crocodile was puzzled. His wife continued, "I want to eat the heart of your friend. I am sure it will be very sweet."

The crocodile was very angry to hear this. He said, "How could you even think of it?

The monkey is my friend. He has been feeding us every day. How could you be so cruel in your thoughts?"

The wife replied, "This is the first time you have refused me something. I am sure the monkey is a female monkey. You are in love with her, and that is why you do not want to get me her heart."

The crocodile said, "You are being foolish! I am not in love with anyone."

"Then get me the monkey's heart!" shouted his wife.

So the crocodile decided to fulfill his wife's wish and went to the tree the next day. The monkey was waiting for him.

He looked at the crocodile and asked, "Why are you looking so sad today?"

The crocodile replied, "My wife is very angry with me. She says we have not repaid your kindness. She has insisted that I take you home for lunch." The innocent monkey said, "So why are you sad about it? I cannot swim, so please carry me on your back."

Thus the crocodile and the monkey set off to the crocodile's home. After they were

mid-way in the water, the crocodile decided to tell the monkey the truth. He said, "My friend, I lied to you. Actually, I plan to kill you, and carry your sweet heart for my wife.

She thinks that your heart is sweeter than the sweet fruits you give us."

The monkey was shocked, but he decided to act calmly. He said, "You should have told me this before my friend. I would love to give my heart to you. But I keep my

heart safely on the tree, so that it does not get lost. I don't have it with me right now."

The crocodile did not know what to do. He could not go back home without the heart. So he said, "What do we do now?"

The monkey replied, "Take me back to the shore and I will quickly get my heart back from the tree." The crocodile believed him and took him back.

The moment the monkey touched the shore, he ran up to the safety of his tree, and screamed at the crocodile, "You unfaithful friend! Go away and never come back! My heart is within me, how can I keep it somewhere else – I would die!"

The crocodile knew he had been tricked, but what could he say to the monkey, because he was the one who had cheated a friend!

# OTHER TITLES IN THIS SERIES

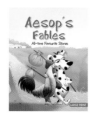     

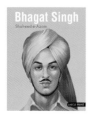  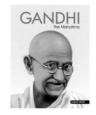   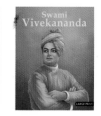

   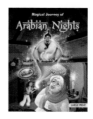